100

Things That Go

Have fun completing this sticker activity book.

Use your pens and pencils to colour the pictures. Where there is a missing sticker, you will see an empty shape. Search your sticker pages to find the missing sticker.

Then, use the card pages at the back of the book to create a cool door hanger and write a postcard for your friends.

make believe ideas

Let's build

What is the tallest
vehicle you can see?

skip

dump truck

backhoe loader

forklift

excavator

dumper

bulldozer

concrete mixer

Chug!
Chug!

crane

Can you find the vehicle that digs big holes?

bucket

wheel loader

road roller

3

To the rescue!

Point to the emergency
vehicle that flies in the air.

siren

police car

life buoy

NYPD

DET. ROBERT PARKER

police boat

Which
two vehicles
move on
water?

ambulance

horse

mounted police

rescue helicopter

lifeboat

helmet

police motorbike

armoured vehicle

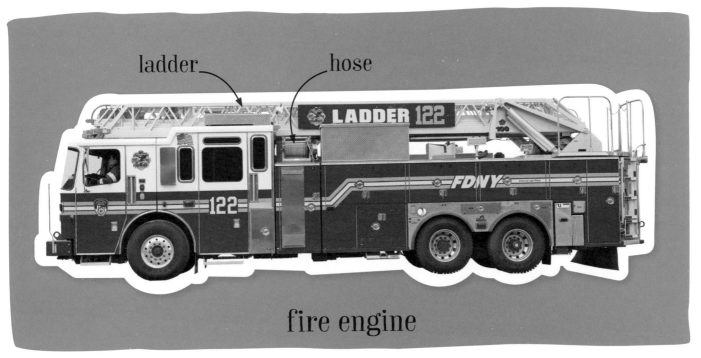

ladder

hose

fire engine

On the farm

How many blue vehicles can you see?

plough

baler

quad bike

crop sprayer

exhaust

Point to the tractor that you like the best.

tracks

steps

giant tractor

tractor

combine harvester

In the air

What vehicle takes
you on holiday?

helicopter

basket

hot-air balloon

parachute

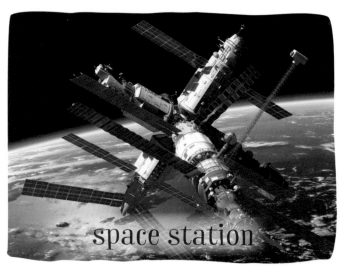
space station

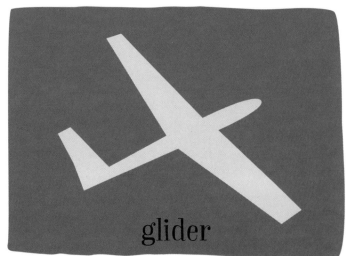
glider

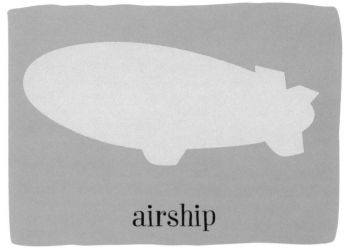

satellite

airship

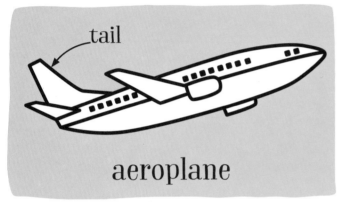

tail

aeroplane

engine

jet

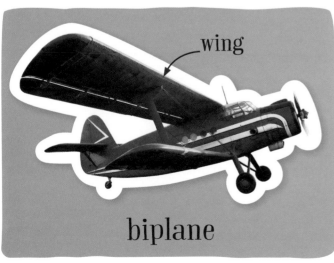

wing

biplane

Find the vehicle that could take you to the moon.

spacecraft

At sea

Where is the boat that goes underwater?

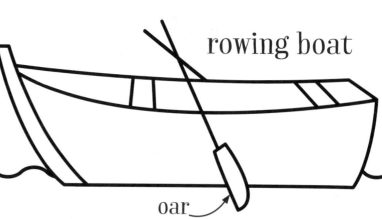
rowing boat

oar

hovercraft

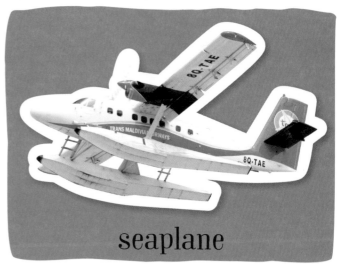
seaplane

deck

cruise ship

hull

yacht

Jet Ski

dinghy

speedboat

ferry

Which boat goes very fast?

mast

sail

sailing boat

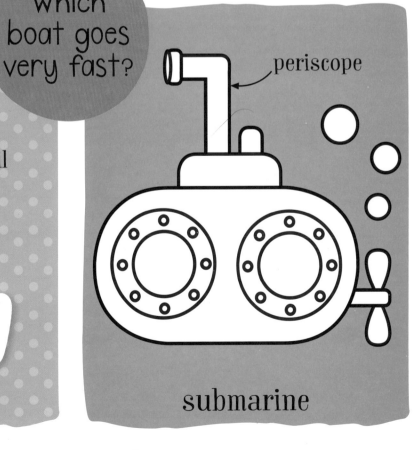

periscope

submarine

In the snow

Which snow vehicle
looks the most fun?

cable car

snowmobile

4x4

cable

ski lift

snowcat

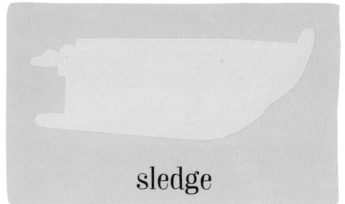

sledge

nose

tail

snowboard

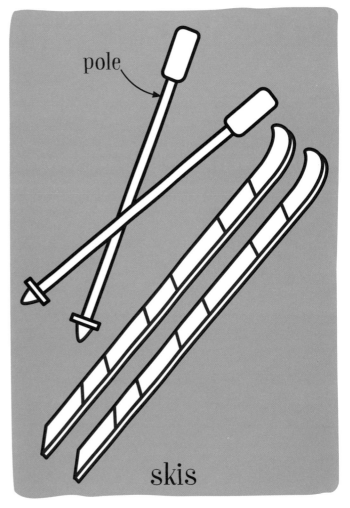

pole

skis

What takes you to the top of a mountain?

snowplough

Busy city

What noise does a train make?

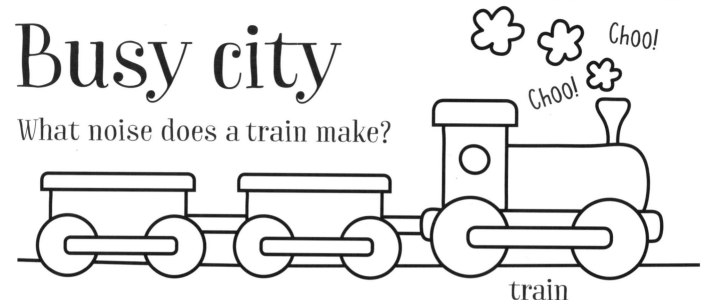

train

scooter

car

light

Point to the vehicles that carry more than four peope.

underground train

bicycle

carriage

tram

fuel tank

tyre

motorbike

van

taxi

school bus

Trucks

Do you have a
favourite truck?

big rig

grille

truck

car transporter

dustcart

Colour the
truck and
the big rig!

tanker